A LITTL

by The Web of Hope

Compiled by Rory Spowers

Edited by Tim Willmott

www.thewebofhope.com

The Web of Hope shows us that 'another world is possible'. It is precisely the sort of initiative which is required right now, mainstreaming the solutions which we so urgently need to implement if we are to build a sustainable future for the planet and for our children.

Zac Goldsmith
Editor of The Ecologist

I admire very much what you are doing.

Tim Smit
The Eden Project

If there's one thing in short supply these days it's Hope. The Web of Hope is just what we all need, highlighting working solutions to the problems that confront us all, proving that together we can make a difference.

Rose Gray and Ruth Rogers
The River Cafe

Either we have Hope within us or we do not. It is a dimension of the soul and is not essentially dependent on some particular observation of the world. Hope is an orientation of the spirit, an orientation of the heart. It transcends the world that is immediately experienced and is anchored somewhere beyond its horizons. Hope in this deep and powerful sense is not the same as joy that things are going well or willingness to invest in enterprises that are obviously headed for early success, but rather an ability to work for something because it is good, not just because it stands a chance to succeed. Hope is definitely not the same thing as optimism. It is not the conviction that something will turn out well, but the certainty that something makes sense regardless of how it turns out. It is Hope, above all, which gives the strength to live and continually try new things.

Vaclav Havel

You never change things by fighting the existing reality. To change something, build a new model that makes the existing model obsolete.

Buckminster Fuller

First published in Great Britain in 2003
by Hopesters

ISBN 0 9545133 0 4

Other books by the author:
*Rising Tides – The History and the Future of
the Environmental Movement*
published in the UK by Canongate in 2002

Reprinted 2004

Designed by Paddy Cramsie at *etal.com*
Printed and bound in the UK by J W Arrowsmith Ltd, Bristol
on Fineblade extra

Acknowledgements:
Special thanks to Bill Grace for letting us use his
plate designs as illustrations.

FOREWORD

There's no shortage of people and organisations telling us just how badly we're screwing up our planet. Listen to them all and you'd wonder whether it's worth getting out of bed in the morning.

When I first received a copy of *The Little Book of Hope*, I saw at once a startling alternative to the gloom-mongering. And now I believe The Web of Hope offers the best possible approach to the myriad ecological crises of the age. It celebrates solutions, wherever it finds them on the planet and offers them as guidance and inspiration to others struggling with similar challenges.

This dissemination of the building blocks of ecological sustainability is both generous and ingenious. By identifying local, national and global success stories, it not only provides practical, adaptable models of best practice, it also fuels the vital furnace of self-belief and determination that will forge new and future solutions.

Everyone who makes contact with The Web of Hope becomes part of the solution. The result is an ever-widening virtuous circle of positive change achieved not by conflict, but by example; not by competition, but by mutual support.

The potential is mind-boggling. If you're interested, I would suggest a simple way forward - just stay in touch with the site, and watch it grow. The moment you feel inclined to bring something to it, don't hesitate. Your thought, however small or local, could be the vital link in a chain, completing yet another strand in the web.

Meanwhile, there's lots to inspire and surprise you in this updated reprint of *The Little Book of Hope* – not least the thought that this could be the start of something amazing.

Please help us make sure it is.

Hugh Fearnley-Whittingstall
Dorset, England, April 2003

CONTENTS

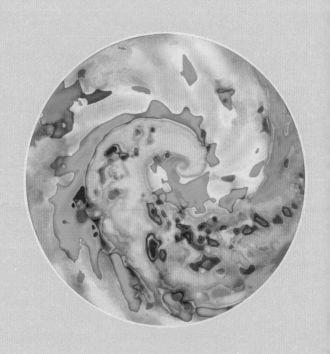

[1]. TRANSPORT

The ability to accelerate a car that is low on gasoline does not prove the tank is full.

The authors of *Natural Capitalism*

The Horrors:

– Cars are responsible for combusting eight million barrels of oil every day, contributing to nearly a quarter of total global greenhouse emissions.

– In America, cars have killed six times as many people as have died in combat during the last hundred years and injured a further 250 million.

– The manufacturing process itself generates more pollution per car than ten years of average driving, with 29 tons of waste generated for every ton of car. Each unit involves the assembly of some 15,000 parts by an industry which uses more resources than any other – 20 % of the world's steel, 50 % of the lead and 60 % of the rubber.

– 40,000 new cars roll off the production line when we go to sleep every night and, in America, there are more registered car owners than registered voters.

– It is now estimated that there are well over half a billion vehicles on the planet which, at current rates, could rise to one billion by 2020.

– Aviation is the worst polluting form of transport per passenger mile, generating nearly as much carbon dioxide each year as the total population of Africa.

– Aircraft produce large amounts of toxic emissions which threaten human health, including nitrous oxides and volatile organic compounds (VOCs), linked to increased cancer rates under airport flight paths.

– Aviation is projected to become the largest single source of greenhouse emissions and already accounts for around 10 % of climatic change. Short-haul flights produce triple the CO_2 emissions per passenger mile as rail travel.

– Airlines pay no duty or VAT on aviation fuel and there is no VAT on either air tickets or new aircraft.

The Hopes:

– *Los Angeles, USA.* In January 2001, the California Air Resources Board voted to go ahead with its Zero-Emission Vehicle (ZEV) mandate. Six major car companies will be required to put between 4,450 and 15,450 electric ZEVs on California's roads in 2003, and progressively increase the number of low-polluting vehicles over the next decade. Ford has issued a statement agreeing to the resolution, the first public acceptance of the mandate by a major car company.

www.zeropollution.com

– *The Hypercar and the Hydrogen Fuel Cell.* Cutting edge 'eco-technology' developments are about to transform not only the basic propulsion systems of the vehicles we drive, but the entire manufacturing process as well. A combination of ultra-light composite materials, low-drag design, integrated micro-electronics and hybrid-electric propulsion, incorporating the hydrogen fuel-cell, is giving birth to a new concept in clean, zero-emissions transport, which minimizes the 'ecological footprint' it leaves on the planet.

At the forefront of this revolution is Amory Lovins, whose Rocky Mountain Institute (RMI) has pioneered much of the research on his Hypercar concept. Lovins and his team realised the intrinsic inefficiency of modern car design, in which the vehicle ends up being twenty times heavier than the driver and needing an engine about ten times larger than average driving requires. From the potential energy within the fuel of a modern car, 80 % is wasted through heat in the engine and the exhaust. 95 % of the remaining 20 % moves the car, while only 5 % moves the driver.

Perhaps the most revolutionary part of the Hypercar concept is the actual drive system, using electricity generated within the car from a separate fuel source, ideally hydrogen fuel cells. The fuel cell was an accidental discovery back in 1839. William Grove, an amateur English scientist and early student of electrolysis, noticed that the process continued to happen in reverse when he disconnected his apparatus. Using a thin platinum-dusted plastic membrane, the fuel cell combines oxygen and hydrogen to create pure hot water and electricity. The mayors of Vancouver and Chicago have been photographed drinking water from the exhaust pipes of fuel-cell buses being tested in their cities.

Natural Capitalism – The Next Industrial Revolution, by Amory Lovins, Hunter Lovins and Paul Hawken (London; Earthscan 1999). *www.hypercar.com*; *www.rmi.org*

– Sustrans, UK. Sustrans, an abbreviation for *sust*ainable *trans*port, is a 'railway path and cycle route construction charity' which has pioneered the traffic-free Greenways routes around the UK, cutting through pollution and congestion to create healthier, safer and friendlier routes for travel. Routes have connected Dover and Inverness, Bristol and London, passing across the Pennines and other scenic parts of the country. The 16 mile Bristol and Bath Railway Path now carries over 1 million journeys per year. The National Cycle Network aims to create 10,000 miles of continuous safe cycle routes, passing through most major UK towns and cities, passing within 2 miles of over 20 million people.

www.sustrans.org.uk

– Curitiba, Brazil. The city of Curitiba in Brazil has a population of over 2 million people and 500,000 cars. A highly efficient, reliable and well integrated transport system however, insures that 75% of commuters, some 1.3 million people, choose to travel by the 'surface metro' bus system, giving Curitiba the cleanest urban air of any Brazilian city.

Jaime Lerner, an architect, engineer and urban planner, became mayor of the city in 1971. Rather than treating urban problems in isolation, Lerner realised the need for a multidisciplinary and systemic approach, seeking synergistic solutions for social, environmental and economic factors issues. For example, the Green Exchange programme placed large recycling bins on the edge of the shanty town *favelas*, where bags of collected rubbish were swapped for food tickets, bus tokens, school notebooks and textbooks. The programme now has a 70% participation rate and the recycling alone saves the equivalent of some 1,200 trees per day.

When Lerner arrived the city was moving towards gridlock. Scrapping plans for an overpass, he pedestrianized the central boulevard and surrounding blocks, where fruit trees and flowers have replaced the cars. Five interlinked axes then formed the structure of the transport system, where double and now triple-length articulated buses collect and drop passengers in seconds from tube-shaped bus stations parallel to express bus lanes.

The whole system is entirely self-financing with a flat rate fare covering the whole city. Fares are distributed to private bus companies proportionate to the number of miles travelled, encouraging wide coverage rather than competition for passengers. The investment required for the system was about 1% of the projected cost for an underground, allowing huge amounts of money to be directed into further social improvements.

www.curitiba.pr.gov.br

– *Ground Floor Partners Initiative, UK.* Members of this national group meet regularly to promote 'best practice' travel plans for their employees. A Nottingham branch of the Boots chemist chain has one of the country's longest running programmes to encourage walking, cycling and car-sharing. An off-road cycle track runs between the city centre and the store, which provides ample cycle parking areas along with showers and changing facilities. The company also invests in staff buses serving 15 locations, while car-sharers are offered priority parking and a guaranteed ride home should the arrangement fall through. The plan has allowed the company to cope with a substantial staff expansion while saving some £160,000 a year in car park maintenance costs.

www.transport2000.org.uk

– *Regional Rail Services, Germany.* Euregiobahn, a new branch line in northern Germany, has brought rail into the heart of Stolberg town centre, where onward flows are fully integrated with 'park and ride' services, cycle parking and local bus timetables. Opened in June 2002, the new trains are carrying 1,200 people per day and rising.

The previously run-down Regiobahn service, running from Kaarst to Mettmann through Dusseldorf, has seen passenger numbers rise from 500 per day to over 15,000. Reacting against plans for closure in the early 1990s, local politicians created a new organisation owned by the town and local 'land councils', run as a not-for-profit company with an emphasis on local management and service.

Again the integration of bus, car and cycle facilities has seen passenger levels continue to rise while the incidence of vandalism falls due to the local community's stake in the railway.

www.euregiobahn.net; www.regio-bahn.de

Watch this space:

– *Bikes and Trains, UK.* There are 22 million cycles in the UK and over 60% of the population live within a 15 minute ride of a railway station. However, less than 1% of British journeys start by bike compared with 15% in Germany and 35% in Denmark. German Railways (DB) started to promote the 'bike-rail' option ten years ago which includes a website search facility for finding services that carry bicycles. The number of bikes carried by train has doubled to 1.6 million per year. Similar schemes have yielded positive results for Swiss Railways (SBB) and the town of Caltrain in California, USA. In the UK, Anglia Railways has pursued a pro-bike policy since 1995, raising capacity for carriage, reducing the charge and promoting cycle tourism from stations.

www.transport2000.org.uk; www.angliarailways.co.uk

[2]. HABITAT

*Modern man talks of a battle with Nature, forgetting that,
if he won the battle, he would find himself on the losing side.*

E F Schumacher

The Horrors:

– For the first time in history, mankind is now a predominantly urban species. Nearly 90 % of the British population now live in urban areas on 7.7 % of the land; two acres of US farmland are lost every minute to urban sprawl.

– A study by WWF estimates that 33 % of the natural world has been exhausted in the last 25 years, largely to supply resources for our cities.

– London's ecological footprint – the impact the city has on world resources – covers 20 million hectares, 125 times its surface area. London consumes 2.4 million metric tons of food per year and requires the equivalent of the country's entire productive land area to sustain itself – 8.4 million hectares.

– Many studies show that modern lifestyles and industrial processes have accentuated the collapse of community spirit and the family unit, leading to the atomised society of today. A study in the US reports that people born after 1950 are 20 times more likely to suffer depression than those born before 1910.

– The number of suspected carcinogens licensed as pesticides in the UK has more than doubled since 1990.

– Fresh Kills, New York's dumping ground, receives 26 million pounds of waste per day. It has become the highest mountain on the eastern coastal plain and one of the largest man-made structures on the planet, covering 2,900 acres of wetland with four pyramids over 400 feet high.

– Over the last hundred years, the petro-chemical industry has synthesised some 10 million new chemical compounds, of which 150,000 have found their way into commercial production and a tiny percentage of which have been thoroughly or reliably tested.

The Hopes:

– The Global Eco-village Network (GEN) was founded in 1994 to support the development of sustainable human settlements, helping to disseminate ideas between eco-villages and making information widely available about their ecological design and demonstration sites.

www.ecovillages.org

– *Chattanooga, USA.* The industrial US city of Chattanooga, Tennessee, developed around coal mines, coke plants, foundries and a federal ammunition plant. By the 1960s the city was suffering mass unemployment due to declining industry, racial tensions from poor housing and a legacy of pollution.

In 1984, civic authorities and business leaders started Vision 2000, a programme involving 1,700 people and 40 projects designed to transform the city. Public and private partnerships raised $790 million to achieve these targets and 37 of them had been realised by 1992. Another 27 goals and task forces were then created, involving 2,600 people. Chattanooga is now regarded as a model of urban sustainability. Virtually the whole population has access to adequate housing, factories for electric buses and carpet recycling have created jobs, a highly effective treatment facility deals with toxic industrial effluent and recycling systems deal with all household waste.

Creating Sustainable Cities, by Herbert Girardet, Schumacher Briefing No. 2 (Totnes, Devon UK; Green Books 1999).

– *Hockerton, UK.* First opened in 1998, the five homes in the Hockerton Housing Project, near the UK town of Newark, are self-sufficient in energy, harvest their own water and recycle waste materials. Using 90 % less energy than a conventional UK home, the houses have been built on a south-facing slope with a triple-glazed solar conservatory to maximize passive solar gains. The earth roofs provide highly efficient thermal insulation, while a mechanical heat recovery system reduces heat losses associated with normal ventilation. The internal temperature remains between 19 and 21 °C throughout the year since the insulating soil stores enough heat during the summer to help warm the house for three months. This self-build co-operative supports its energy needs with an on-site wind turbine and each family expects to save £2,000 a year on the cost of utilities.

www.hockerton.demon.co.uk

– *Auroville, India.* When the first settlers moved out to the South Indian community of Auroville in 1968, they were confronted by a dying habitat. To replenish the soil and conserve water, the Aurovillians dug thousands of kilometres of *bunds*, raised earth banks to hold rain water and control the run-off. This encouraged percolation which re-charged the underground aquifers. An intensive tree planting programme began in the late 1970s, introducing hundreds of species of timber, fencing shrubs, firewood and fruit trees. As the trees grew and the micro-climates formed, many species of birds returned, reflecting the balance of a semi-desert eco-system changing into a forest. Birds and animals have helped the forests propagate and it is estimated that there are now over two million trees on Auroville land, including over 900 species of plant and some 356 medicinal varieties.

www.auroville.org

– *BedZED, UK.* The Bioregional Development Group's Zero-Emissions Development (BedZED) eco-village in South London is a 'carbon neutral' housing project, making no net contribution to global warming from fossil fuel use. Wood chips from an urban forestry programme provide the necessary fuel for a combined heat and power station (CHP) while a car pool scheme (ZEDcars) has reduced car dependence and saved each member an average of £1,500 a year. BP Solar's photovoltaic panels are integrated with double-glazing in the top floor conservatories, generating electricity while providing shade and preventing over-heating in the summer. The electricity will power 40 electric vehicles from a variety of car-charging points, each providing 8,500 kms per year of carbon neutral driving.

Rainwater is harvested from the gardens and roof surfaces, stored in tanks in the foundations of the terraces, then used for flushing toilets and irrigating gardens. A Living Machine (see Water) reedbed system treats sewage on site, recycling it for flushing toilets again. Combined with water-efficient appliances like dual-flush toilets, BedZED has reduced mains water usage by 40%. Other initiatives include a sustainable local paper cycle involving Bioregional Minimills, hemp cultivation for clothes and barbecue charcoal from coppiced woods in Croydon, supplied to local shops through the Bioregional Network.

Initial estimates suggest that by simply living at BedZED, without any major lifestyle changes, residents have reduced their 'ecological footprint' (see Economics) by one third from the UK average. Those that join the green lifestyle services – ZEDcars and local organic food – or work in an energy and paper-efficient office like those on site, can reduce their 'footprint' to the fair-share target of 1.9 average global hectares.

www.bioregional.com

HABITAT

Bioregional Solutions – For Living on One Planet.
Schumacher Briefing No. 8 (Totnes, Devon, UK;
Green Books 2000).

Watch this space:

– *Biomimicry, US.* The term Biomimicry is drawn from
bios, meaning life, and *mimesis*, to imitate. Pioneer Janine
Benyus describes it as 'a new science that studies nature's
best ideas and then imitates these designs and processes
to solve human problems'. Benyus sees animals, plants
and microbes as the consummate engineers: 'After 3.8
billion years of research and development, failures are
fossils, and what surrounds us is the secret to survival.'
By studying these natural processes and systems, biomimicry is showing us how to 'harness energy like a leaf,
grow food like a prairie, build ceramics like an abalone,
self-medicate like a chimp, compute like a cell, and run
a business like a hickory forest'.

One example of how biomimicry could transform the
approach to design is the comparison between the modern
high-tech material Kevlar and the silk of a spider's web.
The production of Kevlar is extremely energy intensive
and creates highly toxic by-products, involving petroleum
based molecules in vats of sulphuric acid, which are pres-
surised and subjected to high temperatures. In comparison,
the waterproof silk spun by a spider, manufactured at
room temperature, in atmospheric pressure and without
toxic chemicals, is five times stronger than steel.

Exponents of biomimicry believe there is huge potential for a wide-range of design applications, from architecture to agriculture: 'We can look at solar-powered transpiration in trees as a means to silently move tons of water up hundreds of feet, at how mangroves desalinate water, and at how termites thermo-regulate their shelters through structural design.'

By replicating the prairie's perennial polycultures, biomimicry could create an edible landscape of plants that would over winter, eliminate the need for ploughing and planting, reverse the trends of soil erosion and phase out the need for chemical applications. The mixture of crops would reduce pest damage and include species which fix nitrogen in the soil.

www.biomimicry.org

– Cradle to Cradle Design, US. The US company McDonough Braungart Design Chemistry (MBDC) have integrated the principles of biomimicry in their Cradle to Cradle Design process, which 'seeks to design industrial systems that emulate the abundance of nature'. They see the 'next industrial revolution' being the application of these principles to design buildings that, like trees, produce more energy than they consume, accrue and store solar energy and purify their own waste water; factories where effluent water is cleaner than the influent; products which do not become landfill waste but decompose as food for plants and animals, helping to rebuild soil. By treating waste as food, the Cradle to Cradle process

emulates natural processes and makes 'zero-waste' an achievable goal.

www.mbdc.com

– *Home-in-a-box, UK.* A house that four people can build in two weeks – that's the aim of Simple Shelter's House in a Box project, which has been occupying a sculptor/ model-maker and an environmental consultant for the last three years. It has come together as a lightweight soft-wood timber construction in kit form, with no parts that four people could not carry, and no need for solid or even level foundations. It arrives on site, complete with all the tools you need to erect it, in a standard steel shipping container which then serves as a lock-up during the construction phase. In addition, a 1:10 scale model is planned, which prospective purchasers could borrow to practise on before launching into building the real thing.

www.schumacher.org.uk

[3]. ENERGY

If economic growth is founded on an ever-increasing reliance on chemicals, toxins, poisons, and energy by-products, then we will choke on the growth that is supposed to save us.

Paul Hawken

The Horrors:

– We now consume as much oil in a year as it takes Nature one million years to create. In 2000, the world consumed 28 billion barrels of oil, some 76 million per day at $27 each – a total of $756 billion over the year.

– By burning fossil fuels, human interference in the natural carbon cycle has increased carbon dioxide in the atmosphere from 285 parts per million (ppmv) to 365 since 1850. The current total of 6 billion metric tons of carbon must be reduced by two thirds if concentrations are to be stabilised below 500 ppmv.

– Various studies suggest that 550 ppmv, a doubling of pre-industrial levels, is an upper limit which cannot be exceeded without triggering a series of 'positive feedback loops', like releasing methane stored as hydrates in the tundra and ocean floors, thereby leading to 'runaway climate change'.

– This would require a country like the UK to reduce greenhouse emissions by a factor of 7 times.

– Americans spend $500 billion on energy each year; their per capita consumption is 5 times that of any other nation.

– During the course of one year, BP spent more on developing their eco-friendly logo than on renewable energy.

– Air conditioning accounts for 16% of electricity use in the US, costing more than the combined GDP of 42 African countries.

– The average annual bill for powering America's jacuzzis is $200 million.

– Two billion people rely on wood and charcoal for their cooking needs and population growth combined with the inefficient conversion of wood to charcoal means that annual consumption is outstripping forest regeneration.

www.campaignagainstclimatechange.net

The Hopes:

– *Alternative Energy Sources.*

1) Solar:

● as much solar energy falls on the planet in one hour as the total human population uses in one year;

● since photo-voltaic cells rely on light rather than heat, studies show that even cloudy climates like southern England could generate some 80% of household electricity from solar power;

• in Norway, 50,000 homes are powered by photo-voltaic cells and more houses in Kenya receive their electricity from solar panels than the national grid;

• photo-voltaic solar technology is now fifty times cheaper than it was in the 1970s and is now available in a variety of forms: for example, four hundred square metres of solar roof shingles exposed to six hours of sunlight can power an average home.

www.ises.org

2) *Wind:*

• over 100,000 families in Denmark are members of wind energy co-operatives which have installed over 80% of all Danish wind farms. The country now receives 15% of its electricity from wind power and the turbine industry employs over 15,000 people.

www.awea.org; www.ewea.org; www.canwea.org; www.auswea.org

3) *Wave:*

• it has been estimated that the UK could generate its entire electricity requirements by tapping just 1% of the wave energy around the coast. The world's first commercial wave power generator has been operating on the Hebridean island of Islay since October 2000.

www.wave-energy.net.

4) Bio-fuel:

• it has been suggested that 5.5 million hectares, some 30% of UK agricultural land, could be devoted to energy crops, providing two thirds of the country's electricity. The UK's Royal Commission on Environmental Pollution reports that this would be more effective than afforestation 'carbon sink' programmes since the sustained planting of 30,000 hectares per year would sequester less than 2% of UK fossil fuel emissions.

www.r-p-a.org.uk

5) Hydrogen Fuel-cell:

• Mercedes Benz have bought a quarter interest share in Ballard, a Canadian company which has become the market leader in fuel cell production, and manufacturers predict that the first zero-emissions hydrogen powered cars will be commercially available within three years. Daimler plans to be producing 100,000 fuel cell engines a year by 2005;

www.ballard.com

• to avoid using non-renewable resources to manufacture hydrogen, researchers in California are developing ways to extract the gas as it is formed by algae exposed to sunlight. Estimates suggest that a small commercial pond could produce enough hydrogen to power a dozen cars indefinitely.

www.hfcletter.com

6) Energy Conservation:

• efficient thermal insulation and double-glazed windows can produce more energy than the oil reserves in the Alaskan Arctic National Wildlife Refuge at its most optimistic projections, at about one twentieth the cost, with four times the employment per unit of energy conserved versus the energy consumed by burning oil.

www.solarcentury.co.uk; www.rmi.org

– *Sun Ovens.* In 1986, Tom Burns, from Milwaukee USA, recognising the need for an alternative cooking system, developed a device which utilises the original energy source of the planet – the sun. The resulting Sun Ovens are the most effective solar powered cookers in the world and have already made a positive impact on deforestation: a family of six using a Global Sun Oven for 80% of their cooking needs saves 4,800 pounds of wood per year. Each oven lasts for 20 years, eliminating the need to cut down thousands of trees. The Global Sun Oven weighs just 21 pounds and can fold up to the size of a small suitcase. The mirror finished anodised aluminium reflectors are super-efficient and enable the oven to reach temperatures of 400 °F within 20 minutes.

The Villager Sun Oven is a larger trailer version, used in large-scale feeding programs. It can reach temperatures of up to 500 °F and bake 50 loaves of bread an hour, or cook two meals a day for a village of 400 people, saving 340,000 pounds of wood a year. Even in sub-zero air temperatures, the oven will capture the sun's rays as if it were a tropical day – as long as the sun is shining. Villager Sun Ovens are now being used across the globe, from an orphanage in Uganda to a co-operative bakery in Honduras. The company has also started manufacturing facilities in Ghana, Uganda, Honduras, Eritrea and the Soviet Republic of Georgia.

www.sunoven.com

– *Local Energy Initiatives.* Researchers a the Kigali Institute of Science and Technology (KIST) in Rwanda have reduced wood-fuel use by 75% with their simple but highly efficient wood stoves. Students at Rwanda's Butare University have also been working with KIST to produce compost from bio-gas residue which boosts crop production by up to 7 times.

www.kist.ac.rw

In Kenya, a small company called Chardust has developed a method for turning charcoal dust into fuel-efficient 'briquettes' for use in improved cooking stoves. The dust is sieved, milled, mixed with a small amount of clay and water to bind it, then passed through a 'sausage-machine' device to make the 'briquettes'.

www.chardust.com

Also in Kenya, the RETAP group has initiated a scheme which provides schools with super-efficient stoves and high-yielding eucalyptus seedlings which meet all their fuel needs. Through a revolving fund, the school can recoup costs through savings on wood fuel, paying back the loan over a couple of years.

povertystores.energyprojects.net

In the Indian state of Maharashtra, the Appropriate Rural Technology Institute (ARTI) have devised a highly efficient kiln which turns sugar cane waste into charcoal and can be used in the field. Their stove and cooker systems cost about £5 and are 4 times more efficient than conventional types.

www.members.tripod.com/ARTI-India

– *Holsworthy Biogas, UK.* A biogas plant, powered by methane from fermented slurry taken from 30 local farms, may soon be providing all the electricity for the town of Holsworthy in Devon, plus hot water for local heating. The resulting pasteurised manure is returned for farm use at the end of the process. The technology was pioneered in Germany where 20 large-scale dung-driven power plants are already operational.

www.farmatic.com

Watch this space:

– *The Salix Project, Wales, UK.* Short rotation coppice (SRC) crops, like poplar and willow, provide a renewable energy source that burns with no net increase in carbon dioxide. Willow is a hardy crop, requiring less input than conventional arable farming systems, cleans waste-water through bio-filtration and works well in neglected or degraded upland areas. As well as supplying energy to the local community, or the farm itself, it can be used for large-scale energy production to supply the national grid. The crop can also supply local markets for willow sculpture, basket-weaving and 'living wood' products used for river bank stabilisation. The Salix Project promotes the use of willow on farms in upland Wales and its value as an energy crop.

www.salix.org.uk

– The International Carbon Bank and Exchange (ICBE). Trading in carbon dioxide emissions involves moving a reduction in emissions output from one party to another. The reduction is then subtracted from that party's total output. The buyer uses this reduction to achieve a legislative or voluntary cap on their emissions. Market mechanisms thus drive emissions down and finance the shift to cleaner energy.

The ICBE provides a platform for individual and corporate clients to keep track of greenhouse gas emissions by using their account to establish baselines and introduce emission reductions. Emission Reduction Credits (ERCs) are issued after certification of renewable energy activities and conservation processes, which can be banked, retired, or made available to consumers and industry. Revenue from ICBE services is then used to finance renewable energy systems.

www.icbe.com

– Contraction and Convergence. Developed by Aubrey Meyer and the Global Commons Institute (GCI), the Contraction and Convergence (C&C) model is perhaps the most simple yet sophisticated framework which tackles the seemingly impossible task of stabilising carbon dioxide emissions and averting the irreversible trends of 'runaway climate change'.

Global surface temperature has risen 0.9 °C between 1860 and 2000. If C&C produced a 60 % cut in annual emissions by 2100, carbon dioxide concentrations can be stabilised at 450 ppmv, 70 % above pre-industrial levels, producing a total temperature rise of 1.5 °C. If trends continue as Business-As-Usual (BAU), the insurance industry estimates that global economic losses from climate change will exceed global GDP by 2065.

The difference between BAU and C&C represents the opportunity for renewable energy and zero emissions technologies worth trillions of dollars per annum – the biggest market in history.

Contraction and Convergence – The Global Solution to Climate Change, by Aubrey Meyer, Schumacher Briefing No. 5 (Totnes, Devon, UK; Green Books 2000). *www.gci.org.uk*

[4]. WATER

*Only when the last river has been poisoned, the last tree been
cut down, the last fish has been caught; only then will you
realise that money cannot be eaten.*

Cree Indian saying

The Horrors:

– Thirty one countries with a collective population of half
a billion are experiencing chronic water shortages. Within
25 years this could reach 3 billion people, 30% of the projected world population in 50 different countries, mainly
in Africa and South Asia.

– Average global water consumption ranges from 5.4 litres
per day in low rainfall countries like the western Sahara, up
to 500 litres per person per day in the US. One flush of a
standard US toilet uses more water than most individuals
and many families in the world consume in a day.

– One in three people in the developing world do not
have access to a safe and reliable water supply – some
1.2 billion. Lack of safe drinking water means that water-
borne diseases account for 80% of all illnesses in developing countries.

– The WHO estimates that 10 million people are dying
every year from polluted drinking water.

– It takes 25,000 gallons of water to make one car and 100 gallons to make a cotton T-shirt.

– According to the UN's Food and Agriculture Organisation (FAO), 15,000 cubic metres of water can sustain 100 families in a developing country for three years, or 100 guests in a luxury hotel for 55 days.

– Nearly half the world's major rivers are going dry, or are badly polluted. Some rivers in Taiwan are polluted to the point of being combustible and 80% of the rivers in China no longer support fish life.

– The huge Ogallala aquifer, which supplies water for American farms from West Texas to South Dakota, is being depleted eight times faster than nature re-charges it. The underground water table has dropped by more than 30 metres in parts of Texas, Oklahoma and Kansas – three key grain-producing states – and wells have gone dry on thousands of farms in the southern Great Plains.

The Hopes:

– *US Water Conservation.* According to a US Geological Survey, per capita water use in the US dropped by 20% between 1980 and 1995.

– Industries in California have made savings of up to 90% in water use through conservation measures like recycling cooling water, monitoring for leaks, changing water nozzles to reduce flow rates, and switching from continuous to intermittent flows in some manufacturing processes.

– A steel plant in the US cut water use by 80% in two years, saving $50,000 a year through the implementation of conservation strategies like replacing drinking fountains with water coolers, fixing leaky pipes and recycling rinsing water.

– A Las Vegas hotel cut its energy and water costs by $70,000 a year by giving guests the choice about whether or not they wanted clean sheets and towels every day. The majority said no, water use fell, sheets lasted longer and pollution declined.

www.waterwiser.org

– *Ryan's Well, Canada and Africa.* After hearing about the water crisis in parts of Africa, six year old Ryan Hreljac, from a small town near Ottawa, decided to try and help. His teacher told him that $70 would pay for a well, which Ryan raised in four months through doing extra chores for his parents. After delivering his donation to the Watercan aid programme, Ryan discovered that $70 would only pay for a hand pump, but $2,000 would drill a well. The Canadian International Development Agency (CIDA) agreed to match funds by 2:1 and Ryan raised the rest, collecting donations from friends, family and local schools. The well was subsequently dug near the school at Angolo in north Uganda, a village whose closest water used to be five kilometres away.

Ryan's original $70 fund-raising has now grown to a

foundation worth $750,000, providing clean water and related health services to people in Uganda, Nigeria, Tanzania, Malawi and Ethiopia.

www.ryanswell.ca

– *Living Machines, USA.* Ocean Arks International (OAI), founded by the ecological designer Dr John Todd, is a global leader in the field of ecological water purification, developing technologies which replicate and accelerate the processes seen in rivers, ponds and wetlands.

By passing contaminated effluent through a series of tanks, populated with a variety of bacteria, algae, plants and fish, Todd's 'Living Machines' not only provide clean drinking water, but also generate fertilizers and maintain a miniature eco-system in perpetuity. No chemicals are required and some of the systems even double up as miniature fish farms. With a higher degree of bio-diversity than the conventional filtration achieved by a reed bed, the Living Machine treats a much wider range of toxic effluents. Some of the plants, like bulrushes, even sequester heavy metals and secrete antibiotics which kill pathogens.

The machines are capable of treating sewage from anything between one and ten thousand households, with one in Vermont handling 80,000 gallons per day. The systems are equally suited to heavy industry, transforming toxic pollution into a beneficial resource. Over 80 ecological waste treatment projects have been completed worldwide, including municipalities, community developments, agricultural industries, food processors, breweries and cosmetic manufacturers.

www.livingmachines.com; www.oceanarks.org

– The Rain Centre, Chennai, India. In India, rainwater harvesting systems on 83,000 hectares, a little more than half the size of Delhi, could provide clean drinking and cooking water for the entire one billion population of the country. In theory, there is not one out of 200,000 Indian villages that could not meet its drinking and cooking water requirements through harvesting rainwater.

The Indian Centre of Science and Environment (CSE) in New Delhi, in partnership with Akash Ganga Trust, a Chennai-based citizen's action group, opened its first Rain Centre in Chennai. This is a permanent exhibition displaying different aspects of traditional and modern rainwater harvesting systems in India. Visitors can learn about initiatives spearheaded in the city and in the coastal plains.

This comprehensive resource on rainwater harvesting houses a functioning model and features colourful panels and posters on water harvesting in different ecological zones of India. Visitors can watch electronic simulations and 'water scenarios', outlining the availability, rainfall, distribution and water usage in the area. Water testing kits and information on testing water quality are also available, along with a CD Rom presentation that details CSE's campaign on rainwater harvesting, an urban and rural technological database, together with detailed case studies of initiatives and practitioners in India. As part of its outreach efforts, the Rain Centre runs eco-tours for school students.

CSE also established the National Water Harvesters Network (NWHN) which promotes a people's water management programme based on water harvesting. It has members and affiliates all across India, all working to achieve this goal.

www.cseindia.org; www.rainwaterharvesting.org

Watch this space:

– *The Water Stewards Network.* By building a global network of innovative ecological thinkers and water practitioners, the Water Stewards Network aims to formulate and implement sustainable alternatives to current patterns of water use in global food production, sanitation and industry, enabling communities to heal damaged water systems through 'their own intelligent and responsible plans of water stewardship'.

www.waterstewards.org

[5]. ECONOMICS

Growth for the sake of growth is the philosophy of the cancer cell.

Edward Abbey

The Horrors:

– In 1960, the poorest 20% of the global population received 2.3% of global income. Today that has dropped to little over 1%.

– The combined wealth of the 350 richest people exceeds the net worth of nearly half the human population.

– The 7,000 trans-national corporations (TNCs) recognised by the UN in 1970 has grown to 44,000.

– Over half of the largest economies in the world are now corporations not nation states.

– The tobacco giant Philip Morris has annual sales greater than the combined GDP of 148 countries.

– 500 corporations control 70% of world trade.

– Economic losses from climate change are predicted to eclipse total global GDP by 2065. Studies by the insurance company Munich Re suggest that there were 20 natural catastrophes between 1950 and 1959, costing the world $38 billion. Between 1990 and 1999 there were 82 catastrophes, costing $535 billion.

– The average European cow receives $2.20 (£1.40) a day from the taxpayer in subsidies and other aid. Meanwhile 2.8 billion people live on less than $2 per day, 1.3 billion on less than $1.

– The US exports 60% of its food, yet 26 million Americans need food handouts. India has a record grain surplus of 59 million metric tons, yet tens of millions of Indian children remain undernourished.

The Hopes:

– *Greening the Tax System.* By shifting taxes in new directions, the overall tax burden remains the same but environmental benefits can be brought into synergy with social and economic goals. Since 1996 the Netherlands has raised some $900 million annually through a gas and electricity tax, returning it with cuts in Social Security payments.

Paul Hawken has highlighted the concept of 'Negawatts', the ability for industry to harness efficiency, use less energy and generate fewer hydrocarbons in the atmosphere. He points out that this would be 'the first time in the history of industrialism that a corporation has figured out how to make money by selling the absence of something', suggesting that oil companies could invest in energy efficient eco-technologies within taxpayers homes, like superglazed windows, and in return receive a return on their conservation investment through Green Fees, calculated upon the barrels of oil that are saved not consumed.

The Ecology of Commerce: A Declaration of Sustainability,
by Paul Hawken (NY; Harper Collins 1994).
www.neweconomics.org

– Alternative Currencies. One of 2,000 or so local currencies
now in operation across the globe, SEL, the French for salt
but also the acronym for Societe d'Echanges Local, is a
French equivalent to the LETS scheme, hundreds of which
began in the UK in the early 1990s. Over 350 SEL groups
now exist across France, involving 45,000 people.

By trading in Sels in the Pyrenees, or Beacons in Wales,
Bobbins in Manchester, Bricks in London's Brixton or
Bunyas in the Queensland town of Maleny in Australia,
local people keep goods and services circulating within the
community without depending on external inputs. This
bolsters local trade, local communities and local economies,
rather than supporting the corporate global economy.

Wirtschaftsring (WIR) was started in 1934 and is Europe's
oldest barter currency, aiming specifically at micro-busi-
ness. By 1993 it had a turnover equivalent to £12 billion
and 65,000 corporate members, making it so widespread
that it amounts to a virtual parallel with the Swiss franc.

*Short Circuit: Strengthening Local Economies for Security in
an Unstable World*, by Richard Douthwaite (Totnes, Devon;
Green Books 1996).

– Micro-credit Schemes. The Grameen Bank was founded
by Mohammed Yunus, creating an innovative lending
mechanism known as 'micro-credit'. By offering small,

uninsured loans to self-employed women in Bangladesh, the Grameen Bank was able to lift hundreds of thousands from below the poverty line. By using a loan to buy a goat for example, a poverty-stricken family is given the chance to start a sustainable business in selling milk and milk products. Yunus aims to make his system available to 100 million of the world's poorest families and believes that it can help to eradicate the global problem of poverty. Over 200 micro-credit schemes are now operating across the US and the concept has been adopted around the world.

www.grameen-info.org

– *The Natural Step Movement (TNS).* The Natural Step (TNS) movement was initiated in 1989 by Dr Karl Henrik-Robert, a leading cancer specialist from Sweden. TNS supports a shift from linear, polluting processes, which create toxic by-products, to cyclical systems which eliminate the concept of 'waste'. By prescribing four systems conditions, based upon rigorous scientific research, TNS roots sustainability in the basic laws of thermodynamics:

- substances from the earth's crust must not systematically increase in the biosphere;

- substances produced by society must not systematically increase in nature;

- the physical basis for the productivity and diversity of nature must not be systematically diminished;

- human needs must be met worldwide.

Companies like IKEA, Volvo, Scandic Hotels, Electrolux and Swedish McDonalds have embraced the four systems conditions prescribed by TNS, cut their resource use and their waste but boosted their profits.

www.naturalstep.org

– *The Ecological Footprint Analysis.* This ecological accounting tool calculates human impacts on the planet, reflecting the amount of 'bio-productive' space required to sustain a particular activity indefinitely. It can be applied to any lifestyle, activity, business, product or manufacturing process, incorporating not just factors like energy, food and resource use but the biological capacity required to absorb full life-cycle impacts like pollution and waste. The 'footprint' methodology was recently adopted by the Welsh Assembly as its sustainability indicator.

www.bestfootforward.com

– *The Praja Co-operative, Nepal.* Formed in March 1999, the Praja Co-operative provides members with a sustainable source of income from producing and marketing Non-Timber Forest Products, including three ayurvedic herbs for The Body Shop. The 200 members come from nine Community Forest User Groups, hailed internationally as a good example of sustainable forest management. The co-op represents the Chepang ethnic group, one of the most marginalized people in one of the world's poorest countries.

– *Teddy Exports, India.* Teddy Exports has been producing wooden massage products for The Body Shop since 1993 and now includes cotton items and hair accessories. As well as providing safe and stable employment for 300 people, The Teddy Trust has set up a school, AIDS aware-ness initiatives, health education and veterinary services within the local community.

www.thebodyshop.com

Watch this space:

– The International Simultaneous Policy Organisation (ISPO). Working from the premise that competitive market forces prevent any significant improvement in the world's social, environmental and economic problems, ISPO suggests that the framework itself needs to change: 'Global de-regulated capital flows and corporations know no national boundaries and, by their ability or threat to move elsewhere, force nations to compete with one another for capital, jobs (and therefore votes) and ever scarcer natural resources.' The Simultaneous Policy (SP) comprises a series of measures by which voters can regain control over transnational organisations and world monetary systems through simultaneous legislative action across national borders. ISPO's growing network of national organisa-tions and local groups aims 'to offer you the beginnings of a new, non-party international politics of co-operation'.

www.simpol.org

[6]. BIODIVERSITY

*Man did not weave the web of life; he is merely a strand in it.
Whatever he does to the web, he does to himself.*

Chief Seatl

The Horrors:

– Net Primary Production (NPP) – the total photosynthetic
production of the planet – is estimated to be 225 billion
metric tons of wood, grass, fibre and food. The human
economy utilises, consumes, converts, burns or clear-cuts
40% of NPP on land. That means that just one species out
of up to 30 million is using 40% of the planet's production.
This figure is projected to be 80% by 2040.

– At one stage in the late 1980s, deforestation was estimated
to occur at a rate of one football field per second. A recent
study by WWF puts the figure at 37 football fields per
minute, about 64 acres, due to logging, land clearance and
fires. Clear-cutting tropical forests devastates the entire
ecosystem because between 75% and 90% of the nutrients
are tied up in the biomass.

– It is estimated that mankind has driven up to one million
species into extinction during the last decade and that all
of Africa's wildlife will be in danger of extinction within
40 years if present rates continue.

– To date, only 1.75 million life forms have been identified and named, with some 15,000 added annually. Many of the rest will disappear before we even know they exist. One in four mammal species are facing risk of extinction and one in eight birds.

– A single edition of a UK newspaper requires 460 metric tons of paper or 1,384 cubic metres of roundwood. One issue therefore consumes the entire year's pulpwood from 138 hectares of plantation, 43,000 hectares in a year, a forest 12% larger than the Isle of Wight.

The Hopes:

– *Forests.* Forests can be seen as a stock of 'natural capital' which, if properly maintained, will provide products in perpetuity while helping to maintain soil, hydrology and a stable climate.

In the same way that the loss of trees causes systemic impacts, the planting of trees helps to encourage systemic benefits:

• providing shade and moderating high temperatures in hot countries;

• absorbing carbon dioxide and other airborne pollutants as part of their respiratory photosynthetic cycle, generating oxygen in the process;

• preserving moisture in the soil and preventing erosion;

• providing habitats for many species and promoting the

beneficial relationships of bio-diversity within a complex system;

• performing a crucial role in agro-forestry systems which could help us produce much more food from much smaller areas.

– *Trees For Life (TFL), UK.* In the Highlands of Scotland, only 1% of the Caledonia Forest remains, the peat preserved tree stumps indicating that this was once a forested area which was denuded by man. In conjunction with various landowners and the UK Forestry Commission's agency Forest Enterprise, the Trees For Life (TFL) project has started to reverse this process, planting native tree species like the Grand Scots pine, the backbone of this forest eco-system, along with birch, alder and rowan. This ambitious project hopes to reforest a 1,500 square kilometres of the north-central Highlands and reintroduce extinct native species like the wolf, lynx and elk.

So far, over 100,000 naturally-regenerating Scots pine seedlings have been protected from over-grazing, more than 93,500 native trees have been planted and 159 hectares fenced for forest regeneration. Much of this work has involved volunteers, who receive a powerful wilderness experience while doing something practical for the planet in the process.

www.treesforlife.org.uk

– *Agriculture, Forest Gardens.* Traditional agriculture systems controlled pests through diversification, planting a mixture of crops rather than the intensive monocultures of the modern agri-business. Companion planting, or 'intercropping' a variety of species, not only maintains bio-diversity but has multiple systemic benefits:

- mixed farming helps protect against pests by promoting a dynamic balance between insects and their predators;

- makes use of synergistic properties like deep rooted crops which bring water and nutrients up from below;

- modifies micro-climate conditions like humidity, light, temperature and air movement;

- encourages cross-pollination between species and preserves genetic diversity.

The forest garden concept has been well established in various parts of the globe and there are numerous examples of the high productivity that can be achieved. Rather than felling the existing trees, the Chagga settlers on the slopes of Mount Kilimanjaro planted bananas, fruit trees and vegetables in their shade. Now the individual plots, which average 0.68 hectares in size and contain some 17 vertical layers of vegetation, provide the entire subsistence for a family of ten people.

The south Indian state of Kerala, the most densely populated area in the country, contains some 3.5 million forest gardens. One plot of just 0.12 hectares has been known to contain 23 coconut palms, 12 cloves, 56 bananas and 49 pineapples, with 30 pepper vines trained up the trees.

Associated industries in the area include the production of rubber, matches, cashews, furniture, pandanus mats, baskets, bullock-carts and catamarans, along with the processing of palm oil, cocoa and coir fibres from coconuts. Many families meet their own energy requirements through biomass systems fed by human, animal and vegetable waste, while the forest gardens provide full-time occupations for families which average seven members.

Forest Gardening: Rediscovering Nature and Community in a Post-Industrial Age, by Robert Hart (Totnes, Devon; Green Earth Books 1996). *www.kerala.com*

– *Urban Agriculture.* Urban agriculture can help preserve biodiversity in our cities. There are 300,000 allotments in the UK, covering 12,000 hectares and producing 215,000 tones of produce every year worth £561 million. A system of organically managed food and garden plots could act as 'green corridors', drawing extra wildlife into the city landscape.

The residents of Apple Tree Court, a housing estate in Salford, an inner city area of Manchester, dug up the barren lawn surrounding the block, laid out vegetable beds, planted fruit and nut trees, created a wildlife area, dug a pond and put in outdoor seating. By involving the whole community, the project deterred acts of vandalism. A flourishing co-op was born after the estate's first harvest in 1995 and plans were activated to use waste heat from the building to grow food in polytunnels on the roof.

The project has since expanded to include a training programme for up to twenty young unemployed workers,
involved in gardening, landscaping and recycling activities,
as well as giving assistance to primary school teachers in
establishing a mini 'urban oasis'.

This work is to be extended by the partnership to include
step-by-step demonstration days for visiting tenant
groups, aiming to share the project's practical experience
of creating sustainable environments in and around high-
rise blocks of flats, from developing orchard and allotment
layouts to starting up a community cafe and growing
mushrooms in basements and trees on window sills.

www.cityfarmer.org

– Navdanya, India. Since 1987, the Navdanya programme
has been saving seeds, promoting organic farming methods,
raising awareness on the hazards of bio-safety, genetic
engineering and bio-piracy, thereby defending people's
traditional food rights and food sovereignty in the face of
globalization. Inspired by Indian scientist Vandana Shiva's
Research Foundation for Science, Technology and Ecology,
Navdanya pioneered the seed-saving movement, establishing over 20 seed banks in seven states, serving over
10,000 farmers and saving over 1,500 varieties of rice,
millet, pulses, oil seeds and vegetables.

Navdanya's Biodiversity Conservation and Organic Farm
in the Himalayan foothills has transformed a land deserti-
fied by eucalyptus monoculture into a habitat where more

BIODIVERSITY

than 650 varieties now flourish, including 250 rice varieties, 30 of wheat and many medicinal plants.

www.vshiva.net

– *The Green Belt Movement (GBM), Kenya.* Founded by Professor Wangari Maathai – now the Kenyan Environment Minister – the Green Belt Movement earned its name by encouraging community members to plant trees in large areas of public land. As well as a means of averting desertification, the programme was a response to the need for fuelwood in the home for more than 90 % of the rural population. Over 20 million trees have been planted since 1977, with a survival rate of 70 %. Over 50,000 households were mobilised in the process, along with 3,000 schools. Additional projects include Pan-African Training Workshops, Food Security, Civic Education and the Peace Trees Project, promoting tree planting as a means of conflict resolution within and between communities.

www.geocities.com/gbmovement

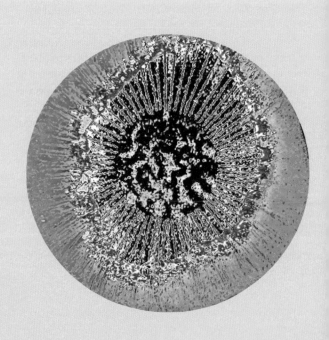

[7]. ORGANISATION

The optimist waits for the wind to change, the pessimist says it won't, the realist sets the sails.

Anonymous

The Horrors:

– The World Bank generates $3 of business for western companies for every dollar lent to the Third World for 'development', allowing $500 billion to flow back to the West in interest and debt repayments for every $50 billion loaned in aid.

– The World Trade Organisation (WTO) incorporates 135 countries and enforces more than 20 international trade related agreements. The agenda is enforced by tribunals composed of three trade bureaucrats who have often had previous legal careers representing corporate clients on trade issues. They meet in secret and have legally binding powers of enforcement, including the right to impose sanctions on offending states.

– The WTO has been described as 'an embryonic world government', but not one electorate has voted for it, nor is it accountable to the public.

– The WTO has ruled against and undermined national laws like the US Clean Air Act and Endangered Species Act, and Japan's regulations on pesticide residues. It has also ruled against an EU ban on hormone-treated beef and the EU's banana importation scheme designed to support small farmers in the Caribbean.

– A recent UK study proved that every hectare of British farmland costs the taxpayer an average of £208 a year.

– A study by the Organisation for Economic Co-operation and Development (OECD) has shown that for every pound given to UK farmers, consumers paid up to £1.80 in higher food prices and taxes.

– The number of Americans suffering from obesity has more than doubled since 1980 and it is estimated to cause 8% of illness-related costs, some $40 billion.

– Americans spend more on fast food than they do on higher education and fast food corporations supply 13% of schools.

www.wtowatch.org; www.globalresponse.org

The Hopes:

– *Kerala, India.* With the first freely elected communist government in the world, the south Indian state of Kerala contradicts many of the current assumptions made about 'wealth', 'quality of life' and 'standard of living':

• despite having an average annual income of around $350 – 70 times less than his American equivalent – the life expectancy for a Keralite male is two years less;

- Kerala's birth rate is falling from 18 per thousand to come in line with the US figure of 16 per thousand;

- as well as providing a model of efficient and sustainable agriculture, producing more than any other Indian state, Kerala is now considered 100% literate, the same as the US and western Europe;

- according to the Physical Quality of Life Index (PQLI), Kerala rates higher than any other Asian country except Japan, despite being one of the most densely populated places on earth.

www.kerala.com

– *Crystal Waters, Australia.* First established in 1987, Crystal Waters in the Australian state of Queensland has since received the UN World Habitat Award for its 'pioneering work in demonstrating new ways of low impact, sustainable living'. The 83 freehold residential and 2 commercial lots occupy 20% of the 640 acre property. The remaining 80% is the best land, which is owned in common and can be licensed for sustainable agriculture, forestry, recreation and habitat projects. The village centre is zoned for commerce, light industry, tourism and educational activities.

The community now involves some 200 people with a multitude of businesses and food producing gardens. The productivity of the land has increased dramatically, while community by-laws ensure that residents are responsible for the provision of their needs and the disposal of waste within ecological parameters. Important impacts include the revitalisation of the local bio-region due to the influx of new residents, increased diversity of flora and fauna, an improvement in land quality, the nurturing of new 'green' technologies and the education of the many course participants and guests that visit the community.

Although the community never aimed to become totally self-sufficient, believing that interaction with the surrounding bio-region is ultimately more sustainable, many people are very self-reliant, growing most of their food and meeting timber requirements for building, fencing and firewood. The community recognises that there will always be imports – for example, fuel and metals which can be substituted in a limited way but not replaced completely – and therefore feels a responsibility to offset these imports with some exports, ranging from fruit and vegetables to knowledge, skills and experiences.

Many of the principles and features of the community are consistent with recommendations in 'Agenda 21', the policies for implementing sustainable development which were first drawn up at the 1992 UN Earth Summit in Rio.

Crystal Waters: *www.ecovillages.org/australia/crystalwaters*

– Gaviotas, Colombia. The pioneers of Gaviotas have already created a legend – a flourishing community within some of the most desolate terrain in the Andes. Inspired by the original vision of Paolo Lugari, a group of professors, students and technicians came together in 1971, taking

up the challenge of creating a sustainable and self-reliant community within some of the most barren and brutal landscapes on earth.

Ground-breaking innovations have included hydroponic techniques to grow food in poor soil; wind turbines that convert mild tropical breezes into electricity; solar panels that work in the rain; ultra-efficient pumps which tap deep aquifers and can be powered by children's see-saws.

The success of Gaviotas has been recognised around the world, making it a role model for sustainability and alternative technologies. 'Elsewhere they're tearing down the forest,' says Lugari, founder of the community. 'Here we're putting it back. If we can do this in Colombia, there's hope that people can do it anywhere.'

Gaviotas – A Village to Reinvent the World, by Alan Weisman (Vermont, USA; Chelsea Green Publishing Co.). *www.chelseagreen.com/Gaviotas*

– The ZERI Foundation. The Zero Emissions Research Initiative (ZERI) uses an 'open systems' approach in which all outputs from any process are turned into useful inputs for another. Founded by entrepreneur Gunter Pauli, the ZERI methodology recognises that nature has no concept of 'waste' and thereby seeks to eliminate pollution from manufacturing processes.

Pauli first hit the spotlight as chief executive of Ecover, producing ecological cleaning products. However, despite making rivers in Europe less polluted, Pauli later realised that he was merely exporting the pollution from Europe to Asia, since for every kilo of coconut palm oil be bought in Malaysia or Indonesia, he left behind 20 kilos of waste. Furthermore, increased demand for the products in Europe led to more destruction of the rainforest in Asia. Pauli now believes that any business which is polluting is merely missing an opportunity for profit.

The elegance of the ZERI approach is illustrated by the concept of 'ecological clusters', creating cyclical networks of associated industries so that the waste from one becomes the raw material for another. 'Ecological clusters' have developed around Colombian coffee farms, where farmers previously used just 3.7% of the plant before burning the waste or sending it to landfill. Now the coffee biomass is used to cultivate tropical mushrooms, feed livestock, compost fertiliser and generate domestic energy. In Brazil, highly nutritious spirulina algae is now being grown in the irrigation channels of rice fields, generating additional income for the farmers since it is then used to enrich a 'ginger cookie' programme in rural schools to combat malnutrition.

In New Mexico, chainsaws lubricated with a liquid containing mushroom spores have been the catalyst for another 'cluster', creating a rich humus on the forest floor, thus providing sustenance for sheep which in turn provide wool for the Tierra Wools Co-operative, a new business making jumpers coloured with natural dyes made from local plants like sage and juniper.

In 2002, ZERI launched a Certification Training programme, teaching individuals, companies and communities 'how to do more with what nature produces rather than asking Nature to produce more.'

www.zeri.org

– World Social Forum (WSF). In February 2002, while the World Economic Forum (WEF) was being held in New York, 55,000 people from 131 countries came together in the southern Brazilian city of Porto Alegre to propose practical alternatives to the current model of neo-liberal corporate globalization. A programme which ran to 150 pages, including some 27 conferences and over 700 workshops, proposed that 'another world is possible', presenting alternative solutions to the world's social, environmental and economic problems.

The World Social Forum (WSF) is not an organisation in the conventional sense, nor a united platform, but an open space for 'reflective thinking, democratic debate of ideas, formulation of proposals, free exchange of experiences and inter-linking for effective action, by groups and movements of civil society that are opposed to neo-liberalism and to domination of the world by capital and any form of imperialism.' The WSF process is not limited to Brazil, with regional, continental and thematic Forums now appearing across the globe and the possibility being discussed of holding the global 2004 event in India.

www.portoalegre2003.org; www.wsfindia.org

Watch this space:

– *The e-Parliament.* A democratic global 'think-tank', the e-Parliament initiative aims to link 25,000 of the world's democratically elected parliamentary members, connecting world public opinion, civil society networks, religious movements and transnational corporations with global policy-making.

In the Parliament itself, world democratic opinion is expressed, synthesized and translated into actionable proposals for global legislators. In the Forum, information, opinion and polling data are provided by social, economic and religious organisations, allowing every participating group and individual citizen to make its voice heard.

The e-Parliament will begin with a simple website, building into a multi-media communications infrastructure including video, audio and access from mobile phones. The parliamentary process will be overseen by a Council of Legislators from all parts of the world and across the political spectrum. A World Future Council (WFC) of distinguished individuals from academia, politics and civil society, will act in an advisory capacity (see below).

www.earthaction.org/e-parl

– *The World Future Council (WFC).* Initiated by Jakob von Uexhull – founder of the Right Livelihood Awards, or so-called Alternative Nobel Prize – the WFC has emerged as a response to the need for 'institutions with the ethical and intellectual authority to guide us through a cultural mind-shift from global consumer to citizen [with] values of Earth democracy, justice and respect for life.'

The proposed Council would consist of respected individuals drawn from 'the wise, the heroes, the pioneers and the young.' It will be linked to the e-Parliament of the world's 25,000 democratically elected MPs (see above), ensuring that these would 'be advised by our wisest visionaries and courageous activists and entrepreneurs when tackling global problems.'

The core Council of about 100 members will be supplemented by advisory circles from different sectors of society and membership would rotate. A database of suggested council members is in preparation and, as a first step, they will be asked to endorse the call for a WFC. Those who agree will be asked to join the WFC or one of its advisory groups.

The core Council will meet annually to hold hearings, commission research and call for specific actions, which can be endorsed by the e-Parliament and brought into national parliaments by MPs for immediate legislative action, backed by the moral power of the WFC.

German SWR TV is committed to transmit open WFC sessions worldwide and the initiative hopes to be operational within 3 years if the required support materializes.

www.worldfuturecouncil.org; www.earthemergency.com

[8]. FOOD

The world has enough for everyone's need, but not everyone's greed.

Mahatma Gandhi

The Horrors:

– Six billion hectares of productive land are being lost to desertification every year and 26 billion tons of topsoil are literally washed out to sea.

– Intensive farming monocultures are not only energy intensive but immensely inefficient, yielding only 6 units of energy in food for every 15 expended in its production.

– By the time you have read this page, nearly 100 people around the world will have succumbed to pesticide poisoning – 48 every minute, 25 million every year.

– UN figures show that global food supplies are more than adequate without the need for GM crops, producing 1.5 times the amount that is required to feed the expanding population.

– Just four companies, Syngenta (formerly AstraZeneca and Novartis), DuPont, Monsanto and Aventis, account for 60% of the global pesticide market, 25% of the global seed trade, and virtually all the transgenic seed currently in circulation.

– Before GM crops were introduced, US maize farmers made a profit of $1.4 billion. In 2001, they lost $12 billion.

– US government statistics confirm that GM crops have led to increased herbicide applications. In 2000, Roundup Ready (RR) maize was treated with an average of 30% more herbicide than non-GM maize.

– The US Environmental Protection Agency (EPA) estimates that 300,000 farm workers suffer acute pesticide poisoning each year.

– The food on an average Westerner's plate has travelled at least 1,300 miles from the field to the table.

– The UN Food and Agriculture Organisation (FAO) has reported a 75% reduction in agricultural genetic diversity during the last century.

– According to the US Food and Drug Administration (FDA), at least 53 carcinogenic pesticides are currently applied in massive doses to major food crops.

www.etcgroup.org; www.ngin.org.uk

The Hopes:

– *Cuba's Organic Revolution.* The Caribbean island of Cuba was threatened with famine when its main sponsor, the former USSR, collapsed in 1991. With a US trade embargo, the island was forced to turn to its own resources, starting a revolution in organic farming which now leads the world. In Havana alone, there are now some 8,000 local organic gardens supplying food for the city. The country now produces more than ever before, using less than half the chemicals. Eddy Menendez, a Cuban agronomist, has proved that seedlings grown with organic waste and worm compost develop healthier root systems: 'There is no need to use any chemical. This is fundamental.'

To help others learn from the Cuban success story, the NGO Food First started a Cuban Farming Exchange Program, arranging visits for farmers and researchers to see the systemic benefits that arise when government incentives support organic techniques and urban agriculture.

A recent report by the World Bank shows that Cuba now ranks first or second amongst all Third World countries in social and economic indicators, which the report regarded to be as a direct consequence of switching to sustainable agriculture methods.

www.foodfirst.org

– The Fukuoka Method, Japan. In Japan, Masanobu Fukuoka has pioneered perhaps the most energy efficient agriculture in the world, growing a variety of crops together but without ever ploughing the land, thus pre-serving soil structure and fertility. The usual crop rotation is replaced by a continuous grain or legume.

In the autumn, rice, clover and another winter grain like rye, barley, oats or winter wheat are sown into the ripe rice crop before planting. After harvest, the rice straw and husks are returned to the field as mulch, while the clover provides a 'living mulch' which continually fixes nitrogen. Winter grains then grow through the mulch and are harvested in the spring when the rice seedlings are small. The rice is then flooded for a week in the summer, which weaken the weeds but does not kill the clover. Then the cycle starts again.

On a quarter of an acre, Fukuoka produces 22 bushels of rice and 22 bushels of winter grains, enough to feed up to ten people and requiring a few days work for one or two people to hand sow and harvest the crop. The Fukuoka system has spread widely though Japan and is now practised on nearly a million acres in China.

One Straw Revolution, by Masanobu Fukuoka (Other India Bookstore 1992). *www.fukuokafarmingol.net*

– *Primrose Organic Centre, UK.* Primrose Earth Awareness Trust (PEAT) is a new initiative launched at a 1.5 acre organic smallholding at the base of the Black Mountains in Wales. The centre sells 85% of its organic produce within five miles, houses one of the largest forest gardens in Britain – with one hundred species of fruit and nut trees – and provides training in sustainable farming practices.

An education programme runs workshops for children of all ages and the centre has plans for an Eco-Sustainable Education Centre built with local and renewable materials – earth, hazel, willow, oak, turf, lime render, wool insulation, straw bales and local stone.

www.primrosetrust.org.uk; www.soilassociation.org;
www.hdra.org.uk; www.fwn.org.uk

– *Permaculture.* Permaculture was first developed in Australia in the 1970s, by Bill Mollison, whose aim was to develop a complete agricultural eco-system, an edible landscape which would encourage self-reliance. Permaculture has been extended to incorporate every aspect of human lifestyles, from alternative energy systems to architectural design, and has been introduced to every type of climatic system on a variety of scales, from Nepalese villages high in the Himalayas to suburban back gardens in Europe. Crystal Waters, in Australia's New South Wales, is a complete community modelled on permaculture principles.

Permaculture recognises that a sustainable agriculture must satisfy four basic requirements:

• produce more energy than it consumes;

• must not destroy its own base, that is to say the soil, local hydrology etc;

• must meet local needs;

• must find its own nutrients on site.

Various natural ecosystems satisfy these criteria, like forests, lakes, swamps and savannah. Traditional agriculture systems have recognised this and therefore endeavoured to replicate, or work with, the inherent energy of the surrounding landscape. For example, farmers in New Guinea, using forests, lakes, pastures and no-tillage techniques, use one unit of energy for every 15 that is produced.

Permaculture systems emphasize perennial rather than annual crops, with tree crops replacing annuals for winter animal fodder and some human food. Trees are amazingly efficient as a source of food, an acre of black walnut trees being 400 times more productive than an acre of wheat. Other important aspects of the design include high species diversity, 'intercropping' and 'companion planting' to encourage symbiotic and synergistic functions. Tomatoes are planted with nasturtiums, comfrey with potatoes for potash, gladiolus with onions against onion rot.

The use of small scale machinery and hand tools is encouraged, along with a combination of gardening, commercial farming, grazing, poultry and aquaculture, the recycling of all materials and an overall design which minimises walking and transportation. For example, the zone around the house is used for crops which require the most attention and are used the most, like annual vegetables and culinary herbs. Beds are planted so that crops which are harvested regularly, like lettuce and salad leaves, are placed in front of those which are picked only once, like cabbages and carrots. Similarly, the orchard is placed beyond the immediate garden, the pasture and forest furthest away. Three dimensional space is also exploited, growing plants of different heights and training creepers up the trunks of trees.

Permaculture: A Designer's Manual, by Bill Mollison (Australia; Tagari 1988). *www.permaculture.co.uk*; *www.permacultureactivist.net*

– The ISEC Roadshow, UK. The International Society for Ecology and Culture (ISEC) promotes locally based alternatives to the global consumer culture. Through a 'roadshow' exhibition of posters and slides, ISEC has been promoting localisation throughout the UK, suggesting ways in which to 'bring the food economy home' by linking producers and consumers through farmers markets and farm shops. In addition, by setting up credit unions, consumer co-operatives and community supported agriculture (CSA) schemes, communities are able to bolster local economies and guarantee food security and quality in contrast to the produce derived from energy intensive industrial farming which creates 'food miles' as it travels around the globe and relies on chemicals, preservatives and excessive packaging.

www.isec.org.uk

– Community Supported Agriculture, (CSA) UK. By offering the local community the option of investing in a share of the harvest before production starts, CSA schemes give farmers a more reliable income, provide direct links with a customer base and spread the risk of a poor season. America has over 1,000 CSA farms, with a combined membership of over 100,000 households and receipts of $50 million a year. The UK's Soil Association is actively promoting a network of CSA farms in the British Isles.

Flaxland Farm CSA, near Canterbury in Kent, has run as a subscription farm since its first season in 1996, supplying a vegetable box scheme to local residents and shops in town. Tablehurst Farm in East Sussex has been registered biodynamic for more than 30 years and is owned by a co-operative of 200 members. In the north of Scotland, locals have bought £500 shares in cows at Wester Lawrenceton Farm to help establish a dairy herd on a Soil Association farm; interest is paid in the form of £40 worth of cheese plus a trailer of manure for their gardens.

www.soilassociation.org

– Becontree Organic Growers (BOG), UK. In East London, a small group of people have transformed local attitudes to the environment, food and health through applying permaculture design skills on an abandoned three acre site. Becontree Organic Growers was formed in 1994, aiming to fulfil guidelines for sustainable urban agriculture presented in Agenda 21. An area previously covered in rubbish and brambles is now home to 17 species of birds, 7 types of butterfly, common lizards, slow worms, foxes, toads and newts, as well as plants like hedge garlic and bluebells. Fresh organic produce is supplied to the neighbourhood, the community composting system has won an international eco-design award and volunteers have come from the University of East London and the British Trust for Conservation Volunteers (BTCV).

www.btcv.org.uk; www.soilassociation.org

Watch this space:

– The SimplyOrganic Food Company. The world's first 'carbon neutral' home delivery supermarket, this mail-order company has been working with Future Forests to calculate the carbon dioxide emissions created by their delivery service and will be planting enough trees to off-set the emissions. The calculations were made by Future Forests at the Edinburgh Centre for Carbon Management and SimplyOrganic customers will be able to make a payment of 10p per delivery to help fund the 66 trees which will be planted annually in five managed public access woodlands across the UK. Future Forests help companies and individuals to reduce emissions as much as possible, having already worked with EMI, Whole Earth Foods, UNISON and the Glastonbury Festival. The trees are managed by a range of organisations including Wildlife Trusts and Community Forests Programmes.

www.simplyorganic.net; www.futureforests.com

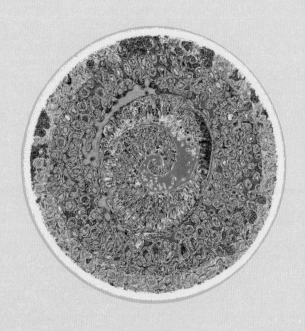

[9]. HEALTH

A multiplicity of hospitals is no test of a civilization. Rather it is a symptom of decay.

Mahatma Gandhi

The Horrors:

– Drug sales in the US suggest that up to 80% of adults ingest at least one medically prescribed drug every 24 hours. An average doctor in the UK National Health Service writes one prescription every six minutes.

– Our food is now grown with, and contains traces of, many chemical substances which hardly existed just 50 years ago: hormones, antibiotics, insecticides, herbicides, fungicides, emulsifiers, antioxidants, nitrites and preservatives. Our drinking water is contaminated with pesticides, nitrates and heavy metals.

– Mother's milk would be banned by the food safety laws of industrialised nations if it were sold as a packaged product. The German Health Agency found that milk from nursing women was 20 times more contaminated with dioxin – a by-product of incinerating plastic – than cow's milk. Some paediatricians now recommend that women stop breast-feeding after 3-4 months.

– In the developed, industrial world, half of the male population is now predicted to contract cancer, while the disease affects one in every three women. Some projections suggest that the disease will be responsible for half the deaths in the western world by 2020. In the US, the systemic impacts of the disease account for some $100 billion every year, nearly 2% of GNP.

– Americans spend $150 billion a year on recreational drugs and more on sex-related 'entertainment' than Hollywood's entire domestic box office receipts.

– By 1970, every person on the planet had traces of plutonium and strontium in their bodies.

– HIV infection in Botswana runs at 39% of the population and life expectancy has dropped from 62 to 37 since the 1980s. The average life-span in sub-Saharan Africa is 47.

The Hopes:

– *Community Health.* The Italian city of Siena has often been cited as an ideal model of a healthy urban environment, having the lowest crime rate of any western city of comparable size. This has been attributed to its unique and decentralised structure of government, involving the whole of society, from the individual to the family and the community, within an ascending structural order.

In contrast to the boroughs of London, or the *arrondissements* in Paris, the *contrada* of Siena are considered to be independent city states and autonomous socio-political units. They have their own flags, seats of government, constitutions, patron saints and churches; their own distinct identities, which gives the inhabitants a sense or civic pride, involvement and belonging, in contrast to the sense of isolation and alienation that many feel within the modern urban environment.

www.provincia.siena.it

– *Alternative Cancer Treatments.* The claims supporting the efficacy of alternative treatments for cancer from around the globe have been well documented:

• Danish doctor Kristine Nolfi cured her own cancer with an organic and raw vegetable diet and continues to heal others at her health farm;

• similarly, Ann Wigmore pioneered and promoted wheatgrass juice after using it in conjunction with an organic vegetarian diet to cure her cancer;

• Dr Max Gerson advocates a similar diet with an emphasis on potassium from the skins of root vegetables, combined with pancreatin, freeze-dried thyroid, niacin, Royal Jelly and B12 injections with raw liver juice, for its huge enzyme content. His techniques have achieved 50 % remission in cases classified as 'terminal' by allopathic doctors;

• some 10,000 Americans are believed to cross the border into Mexico every day to visit holistic cancer clinics which have been virtually eliminated in the US. The Mexican methods place an emphasis on garlic, Vitamin C and hydrazine sulphate;

• in Germany, Dr Seeger combines Royal Jelly with Zell Oxygen, a culture of special young yeast cells which are very high in oxygenating enzymes.

www.positivehealth.com; www.wigmore.org; www.gerson.org

– *Bristol Cancer Help Centre, UK.* Founded in 1980, to pioneer the holistic approach to cancer treatment, the UK Bristol Cancer Help Centre follows the holistic approach, supplementing therapies with specific vitamins, minerals and herbs in conjunction with colonic cleansing, meditation and spiritual healing. The centre is now recognised as one of the leaders in the field.

www.bristolcancerhelp.org

The Roots of Health: Realising the Potential of Complementary Medicine, by Romy Fraser and Sandra Hill, Schumacher Briefing No. 7 (Totnes, Devon; Green Books 2001); *The Ecology of Health*, by Robin Stott, Schumacher Briefing No. 3 (Totnes, Devon; Green Books 2000).

– *Ozone and Oxygen Therapies.* Ozone, hydrogen peroxide and 'hyperbaric' oxygen are being used successfully by doctors around the world to treat cancer, HIV and AIDS, heart disease and other acute and chronic disorders, according to the consumer health organisation What Doctors Don't Tell You (WDDTY).

The report claims that the role of chronic, subclinical oxygen deprivation and its contribution to the development of disease has been known for a number of decades. In 1991,

Dr Michael Carpendale and his colleagues at the Veterans Administration Hospital in San Francisco showed that HIV could be 99% inactivated by ozone therapy without harm to healthy cells. Today, an estimated 9,000 licensed health practitioners in Germany and another 8,000 throughout Europe use ozone. Meanwhile the US Food and Drug Administration (FDA) continues to block human trials and doctors are prosecuted for using it.

www.wddty.co.uk

– Health Action Zones (HAZ), UK. Health Action Zones (HAZs) are partnerships between the UK National Health Service (NHS), local authorities, community groups and the voluntary and business sector. Aimed at parts of Britain with the poorest health, HAZ programmes link health, regeneration, employment, education, housing and anti-poverty initiatives to respond to the needs of vulnerable groups and deprived communities.

The largest and most complex, covering 1.4 million people, is the Merseyside HAZ. In the Huyton area, local people have formed a co-op linking residents with nearby farms to ensure affordable supplies of fresh fruit and vegetables. Residents drop off their orders at a local school and collect the produce later that day. The project was recognised by the Sustainable Health Awards, first launched in the area to highlight community groups and companies making a contribution to health, well-being and sustainability.

www.haznet.org.uk

Watch this space:

– *Sympathetic Resonance Technology, USA and UK.* Various laboratory and clinical trials have shown this proprietary technology (carried in a device called the Qlink) to 'produce a host of beneficial effects on humans, cells and other biological systems'. Through resonance with the bio-field of the organism, the technology promotes *homeostasis*, the optimal equilibrium conditions that life requires. Several trials are underway to investigate a significant range of reported benefits, including better sleep and improved energy levels. There is also evidence that SRT provides protection from 'electro-smog', electro-magnetic fields (EMFs) generated by computers, mobile phones and other electrical devices.

www.clarus.com; www.qlinkworld.co.uk

– *Polycontrast Interference Photography (PIP), UK and India.* Regarded as an effective, safe and non-invasive from of diagnosis and preventative healthcare, the PIP scan Energy Field Imaging System claims to reveal the human energy field, highlighting areas of 'dis-ease' and leading to a holistic assessment of the patient's health on physical, emotional and psychological levels. The process uses a software programme with a video feed, scanning 'energetic and light interference at and above our visual range'. PIP is being used by researchers and institutions around the globe, from the MIT World College Peace Centre in the US to the University of Greece and hospitals in India.

www.theenergycentre.org

– *Mushroom Medicine for HIV.* Inspired by the ZERI methodology (see Organisation), Margaret Tagwira from the Africa University in Mutare, Zimbabwe, has pioneered a new type of mushroom farming, making the substrate from water hyacinth, a fast-growing 'weed' which chokes and stagnates water courses but has valuable applications as a biomass energy source.

Margaret domesticated a local variety of *ganoderma lucidum*, a prime medicinal mushroom, which will be grown by HIV orphans as part of an educational programme. *Ganoderma lucidum* has been used in China for thousands of years because of its ability to strengthen the immune system. The programme will help the children enhance their immune systems without having to depend on expensive medicines developed in the West.

Following her success, tropical mushroom farming was launched in Choco, Colombia, a coastal state where nearly 99% of the population is of direct African descent. A one-week training programme led to the domestication of *auricularia auricula,* or 'Jew's Ear fungus', a nutritional mushroom native to Choco and which grows in abundance. The mushroom substrate will be made from wood dust from saw mills, one of the main sources of river pollution in the area.

www.zeri.org

[10]. OCEANS

We're not borrowing the earth from our children. We're stealing it from them – and it's not even considered to be a crime.

David Brower

The Horrors:

– By 1995, nine of the world's 17 major fishing grounds were in precipitous decline and four had been commercially 'fished out'. The EU began to decommission 40% of its fishing fleet, the Malaysian government halved the number of inshore fishers and Canada laid off 35,000 people in the industry.

– The situation has hardly improved since then, with many of the world's fisheries on the verge of collapse. Blue-fin Tuna and Atlantic Cod have joined the endangered species list, while other white fish like the deep-water orange roughy, which only spawns after the age of 30 and takes decades to build up stocks, are now being fished as a cod substitute.

– Over-fishing creates a vicious circle, yielding major returns to start with but depleting resources in the long-term since it removes the spawning stock. After three years, a fishery which catches 90% in the first year returns the same as one that had caught only 30%. By the following year, the intensive fishery catches 30% less than the sustainable one since it has removed a substantial portion of the spawning stock.

- Two million gallons of radioactive liquid are discharged from Sellafield every day. The incidence of leukaemia in the area is ten times the national average.

– A Greenpeace study reveals that the bed of the Irish Sea is so seriously contaminated by BNFL's Sellafield plant that it should be classified as nuclear waste.

www.greenpeace.org; www.oceanconservancy.org; www.savethefish.org; www.conservefish.org

The Hopes:

– *Sustainable Fisheries.* The decline of world fish stocks can be attributed to the growth of industrial fishing fleets using new technologies and the enclosure of local fishing grounds as part of the drive to divide the global commons. However, many traditional fishing communities around the world evolved certain rules which prevented over-fishing and maintained healthy marine populations in perpetuity:

• from the Marovo of the Solomon Islands to the Moluccan communities of Indonesia and the Cree Indian in Canada, the control of fishing resources was held by clan leaders and councils who decided who could fish where;

• for 450 years, the fixed gear fishery in Newfoundland

caught large quantities of high quality cod and other fish at low cost, without diminishing stocks and providing the economic basis for hundreds of often isolated coastal communities;

• when the Cocamilla people in the Peruvian Amazon noticed that their lake was being overfished by commercial operations from district and provincial capitals, they ruled that only subsistence fishermen should be allowed;

• during the 1950s and 1960s, fishermen in Raritan Bay in New Jersey formed their own co-operative with a system of quotas. Any boat that caught more than its quota was obliged to give the surplus to other less fortunate boats in the co-op;

• about 75% of the estimated 10 million fishermen in the developing world use small-scale, minimum impact fishing technologies;

• Well over 100 million people are thought to be dependent on this small-scale fishing industry for their income. Ghana's fleet of 8,000 canoes catches 70% of the country's marine fish;

• a canoe fisherman using an outboard motor is thought to use one tonne of fuel to catch up to 40 metric tons of fish, while a modern trawler uses the same amount to catch 3-4 metric tons.

– *Surfers Against Sewage (SAS), UK.* The Surfers Against Sewage (SAS) Campaign began in 1990, believing that it was not enough to simply protest about sewage pollution but also provide answers to the problem, calling for 'end of pipe' standards to ensure that all sewage is fully treated before being discharged into an aquatic environment. Some 300 million gallons of raw or partially treated sewage are discharged around the UK coastline every day and two million metric tons of toxic waste dumped in the sea every year. Pressure from groups like SAS led the government to ban the dumping of UK-produced sewage 'sludge' in December 1998.

www.sas.org.uk

– Pacific Fishery Management Plan, USA. The Ocean Wildlife Campaign, a coalition of six US national conservation groups, worked alongside recreational fishing organisations and the Pacific Fishery Management Council to ban 'pelagic longline gear' off the coast of California, Washington and Oregon, safeguarding populations of tuna, swordfish, marlin and shark after overfishing had depleted numbers. The law details specific requirements to rebuild stocks within a set timeframe, minimising by-catch and protecting areas of essential fish habitat.

www.savethefish.org

[11]. PEACE

The most potent weapon in the mind of the oppressor is the mind of the oppressed.

Steve Biko

The Horrors:

– Over $1 billion are spent every day on military weapons.

– Current US defence spending is projected to be $3 trillion over five years; more than the combined GDP of most of the world's developing countries.

– The Pentagon aims to achieve Full Spectrum Dominance (FSD) through the 'militarisation of space' and the control of cyber-space.

– Part of the 'Star Wars' programme, the High Altitude Auroral Research Programme (HAARP) in Alaska, is 'heating' the ionosphere through the use of Extra-Low Frequency (ELF) sound waves.

The Hopes:

– *Sarvodaya Shramadana Movement, Sri Lanka.* Founded by Dr A T Ariyatne in the mid-1950s, the Sarvodaya (Awakening of All) movement began as an 'educational experience' when a group of high school teachers decided to 'translate their convictions into action.' Students from relatively affluent backgrounds were encouraged to start 'shramadana' (Sharing Energy) camps, giving up their vacations to share their time, thought and resources in the country's most marginalized villages. By 1967, 100 villages were involved, building to 1,000 in 1974, 6,000 in 1983 and 10,000 by 1994.

After ethnic riots in the 1980s, Sarvodaya built a truly national organisation which has been actively working for peace and economic self-reliance ever since. A five stage development model introduces Shramadana camps, forming functional training groups according to individual needs, from village elders to children. These groups prioritize their needs, launching projects which increase income generating activities and build self-reliance, sharing any surplus within the community.

In March 2002, Sarvodaya inspired one of the largest peace meditations ever held, bringing 650,000 people together in the sacred city of Anuradhapura. At the same time, Sri Lankan Prime Minister Ranil Wickremesinghe made an unprecedented visit to the city of Jaffna, engaged in a peace process with the 'Tamil Tigers' which has brought stability to the island for the first time since 1983.

www.sarvodaya.org

– Conflict Resolution in Bougainville, Papua New Guinea (PNG).
In March 1989, civil war broke out on the island province of Bougainville in Papua New Guinea (PNG), leading to the death of some 20,000 of the island's 120,000 inhabi-

tants. The trouble had started when rich copper deposits had been identified on the island back in the 1960s, leading to confrontations between villagers, landowners and prospecting geologists. The New Zealand government managed to facilitate negotiations in 1997, starting a peace process that finally led to a workable cease-fire. In August 2001, the Bougainville Peace Agreement was signed and constitutional changes were passed by the PNG Parliament in March 2002, recognising the island as an autonomous province. One key element of the Bougainville success was deemed to be the lack of restrictions placed on those that could attend the peace talks or the time required to reach agreement.

www.c-r.org/accord

– Peninsula Village, USA. In the forested foothills of Tennessee, eight out of ten disturbed, marginalized and drug-addicted young people who pass through Peninsula Village, return to school and find jobs, compared to a rate of two or three in conventional reform centres. The year-long programme takes them through the traditional stages of a Native American vision quest, leaving the old life, patterns and habits behind, crossing a threshold into the unknown and then integrating what they have learnt through helping to heal conflict within communities.

www.peninsulavillage.org

[12]. EDUCATION

When the forms of an old culture are dying, the new culture is created by a few people who are not afraid to be insecure.

Rudolf Bahro

The Horrors:

– Many children in the developed world are able to identify over 1,000 brand logos but fewer than ten local plants.

– Each 330 ml can of Coca-Cola contains 46 mg of caffeine, an addictive stimulant of the central nervous system, cardiac muscle and respiratory system. Trucks carrying the concentrated syrup are legally enforced to display hazardous warning signs.

– The artificial sweetener aspartame, marketed as Nutrasweet and Equal, contains three neurotoxic substances – aspartic acid, phenylanaline and methyl alcohol.

– We fill our fridges with food wrapped in clingfilm, containing phthalate plastic compounds which are thought to be responsible for falling sperm counts. Supermarket shelves are lined with thousands of food products but, upon closer inspection, we find that most of them contain little more than refined flour, sugar, saturated fat, salt and chemical flavourings – a recipe for poor nutrition, heart disease and cancer.

– The average American watches 22,000 TV commercials per year and is exposed to 3,000 marketing messages per day. Some 75% of US commercial TV is funded by the 100 largest of the country's 450,000 corporations and most western children have witnessed over 16,000 murders on television by the time they are 18.

– The average child in Mali attends school for three years, compared to between 15 and 17 years in the developed world.

– According to the World Health Organisation (WHO), 'As many as one billion people, mostly women and children, are regularly exposed to levels of indoor air pollution exceeding WHO guidelines by up to 100 times'. Other EU studies suggest that most of us are confronted by about 300 chemicals on a daily basis.

The Hopes:

– *Gaia Theory*. Although the cosmologies of many traditional tribes revolved around similar concepts, Gaia Theory is the first scientific model to explain the earth and the biosphere as one integrated, self-regulating organism.

By linking factors like plankton in the oceans, microorganisms in the soil and the role of tropical rainforests in maintaining a stable climate, Gaia Theory reveals the global cycles which maintain *homeostasis*, the balanced conditions which life requires.

An exploding human population has combined with certain technologies and activities to have a significant impact on homeostasis, disrupting the systems that support life.

For example, our reliance on fossil fuels has led to increased concentrations of carbon dioxide in the atmosphere, leading to global warming and climate change. To make matters worse, human activities like deforestation create *positive feedback loops*, destroying the habitats which help to 'fix' carbon from the atmosphere and thereby increasing the speed at which global warming occurs.

Gaia Theory therefore, places the human species within the context of a much larger web of life. Rather than promoting apathy by suggesting that there is nothing humanity can do, being accountable to Gaia clearly has strong moral implications. One of the laws of Gaia is that any species that damages its environment makes it worse for its progeny. Therefore, if it continues to do so it will go extinct. The converse is also true. Any species that makes its environment better for its progeny has an advantage.

Gaia: A New Look at Life on Earth, by James Lovelock (Oxford University Press 1979).

– *The Earth Centre, UK.* The UK's Earth Centre has been built on 400 acres of former coal mines and slag heaps in South Yorkshire. The central building in this educational environmental visitor centre is known as The Ark, 120,000 square feet of exhibition space which needs no air-conditioning due to a combination of passive solar design and good ventilation. This includes a labyrinth heat storage system underground, which draws night air down to cool the building in the summer and will circulate warm air trapped by glass to provide heat in the winter. A solar canopy has been designed to span the entrance buildings to the site, with photo-voltaic cells set between two layers of glass to optimise the energy derived from the sun. The centre has its own Living Machine biological waste treatment centre and compost from 12 fish ponds is used on adjoining allotments to produce vegetables for the cafe.

www.earthcentre.org.uk

– *Schumacher College, Devon, UK.* Schumacher College is named after the visionary 'ecological economist' Fritz Schumacher and is a leading international centre for ecological studies, running a variety of residential courses in sustainability throughout the year, as well as a bursary scheme for students.

www.schumachercollege.org

– *White Lotus School Project, Ladakh.* High in the Himalayan kingdom of Ladakh, the Drukpa Kargyu Trust is building a village school for 750 children surrounding the village of Shey. The school is designed like a village with a temple in the centre, surrounded by classrooms, kitchen, dining hall, clinic and cottages grouped around courtyards, where the children live and learn to grow vegetables. Walls are made from traditional mud and stone, large south-facing windows make the most of passive solar gain and photo-voltaic panels provide electricity. The school is being built by the community and hopes to be a model for energy efficient and sustainable building in Ladakh.

Living Lightly, Issue 19; www.positivenews.org.uk

– *The School in the Woods, UK.* The School in the Woods was started with a small group of 6-8 year old pupils in a caravan surrounded by Rocks East Woodlands, a Cotswolds Area of Outstanding Natural Beauty outside the city of Bath. The mixture of broadleaf and coniferous trees shelter secret paths and hideaways, old stone bridges and an overgrown Victorian garden, making it an ideal environment for children to explore and develop their awareness of the natural world. The school's founder, Hedevig Blakstad, observes how the children 'have all chosen a special place in the woods – somewhere that is magical to them. From time to time they will revisit their places, offering gifts such as a flower or poem, collecting treasures from nature, observing changes through the seasons, drawing plants, watching creatures, or just listening.'

Living Lightly, Issue 22; www.positivenews.org.uk

– *Forest Schools, UK.* Inspired by similar schools started in Scandinavia back in the 1950s, the first UK 'forest school' was started at Bridgwater, Somerset, in 1995. In 2002, Jenny Doyle started the Bishops Wood Forest School, providing outdoor learning for large numbers of children, many of whom come from nurseries and primary schools for half a day each week. In addition to spending time in this natural environment, children learn practical skills, learning to handle tools safely, gathering and chopping firewood, hunting for fungi and building camps.

www.bishopswoodcentre.org.uk

– Envision, UK. The Young Envisionaries Award (YEVA) was the first project for Envision, a team of young people 'united by a positive vision for a sustainable future.' A ground-breaking environmental award scheme, YEVA creates a 'non-prescriptive and supportive framework' for young people in schools to take responsibility for sustainability issues. Between 10 and 15 sixth form students create 'Greenteams' to devise and implement inspirational activities. Examples from the Pilot Phase (2001-02) included a recycled fashion show, a globalization debate, classroom recycling and a solar powered installation. Envision hope that YEVA will ultimately become a national programme.

During 2002, Envision teamed up with the Bonani Youth Development Group from Soweto, South Africa, to run the Wilderness Experience initiative for 14 motivated young people drawn from different backgrounds. Those taking part were able to bring their conclusions to the UN World Summit on Sustainable Development (WSSD) held in Johannesburg, engaging with a wider audience and other delegates at the Children's Earth Summit (CES). Through initiatives like these, Envision strives to 'develop frameworks to support individuals in all walks of life to initiate solutions. This in turn inspires others with their capacity to participate in building a sustainable society for future generations.'

www.envision.org.uk; www.yeva.org

Watch this space:

– *Project Carrot, UK.* Holme Lacy College in Herefordshire is set to become a unique study centre set in a 600 acre organic estate. Drawing on the experience of progressive initiatives and international centres of excellence, the project aims to 'develop a dynamic social context within which to strengthen the links between human nature, human health, the health of the land and the natural world'.

Project Carrot aims to make sustainable agriculture a defining feature of the Herefordshire countryside as a model region for Europe. The principles of sustainable land management underlie the curriculum in all courses, while features of its innovative research have included a sustainability audit and an 'ecological footprint' (See Economics) of the county. Project Carrot is a partnership between farmers, Holme Lacy College, the Bulmer Foundation, and the Regional Development Agency.

info@projectcarrot.org

Please plug in and become an active strand by contacting us at: *info@thewebofhope.com*

or write to us at: The Web of Hope, Suite 256, 3 Edgar Buildings, Bath BA1 2FJ, United Kingdom.

WoH currently comprises three strands:

• *A Little Book of Hope* – This little book precedes a series of twelve Little Books of Hope to be published over the next three years. The titles of the twelve core topics correspond to the twelve letters in *T-H-E W-E-B O-F H-O-P-E*.

• *The Web of Hope website* – **www.thewebofhope.com**, the first version of which was launched at the 2002 World Summit on Sustainable Development (WSSD) in Johannesburg, South Africa.

• *The Web of Hope Roadshow* – which will tour the UK from 2003-05, visiting town halls, schools and universities, taking 'best practice' role models into communities and classrooms, using interactive displays, story-telling and performances to inspire their replication.

The roadshow, website and books will provide the blueprint for similar projects in other countries, thereby spinning the web around the globe.

The founder members of The Web of Hope are: Colin Hudson, Rory Spowers, Tim Willmott, Robert Weston.